RALPH MACCHIO
writer

ANDREW WILDMAN
CHRIS BATISTA
pencilers

ROBERT CAMPANELLA
ANDREW PEPOY
MARK McKENNA
inkers

MICHAEL HIGGINS
letterer

GLYNIS OLIVER
KEVIN SOMERS
DANA MORESHEAD
ARIANE
colorists

KELLY CORVESE
editor

BOB HARRAS
group editor

TOM DEFALCO
editor in chief

based on the teleplays by
MARK EDWARD EDENS
JIM CARLSON
TERRENCE McDONALD and
DONALD GLUT

First published in Great Britain in 1994 by Boxtree Limited.
Boxtree Limited, Broadwall House, 21 Broadwall, London
SE1 9PL. A CIP catalogue entry for this book is available
from the British Library. ISBN 0 7522 0892 6.

INTRODUCTION

It's been simply incredible, grabbing onto the coattails of this unique cultural phenomenon called X-Men. Of course, working at Marvel Comics has always had a certain mystique. Baby Boomers fondly remember the Lee/Kirby classics of yore. Today's kids love Ghost Rider and The Punisher. So, if you toil in any capacity at the hallowed House of Ideas, you're perceived as sharing in that cache. It's nice. But nothing could have prepared me for the jolt of notoriety I received once I began my service on X-MEN ADVENTURES. My sister, Maria, was asked by numerous patrons at her restaurant, Fiddleheads, to have her brother autograph countless copies of the comic. My brother, Mike, has likewise had similar requests from many professors at his college, should he deign to name-drop during casual class conversations. Amazing. Some thirty years after their initial conception, the X-Men seems to have woven itself into the fabric of everyday life. Media attention, merchandising, licensing, you name it, the mutants are there. People are fascinated by their exploits and the underlying mythology which permeates their world. But nowhere do our colorfully costumed misanthropes receive greater exposure than in their top-rated Saturday morning television series, on which our X-MEN ADVENTURES comic is based.

When X-Men editors Bob Harras and Kelly Corvese first spoke to me about adapting the show, I suspected it would be a daunting though fun task. It's trickier than you might imagine turning scripts for a half-hour animated series (many of which are derived from our own X-MEN books) into a workable twenty-two page comic. Often scenes have to be trimmed, compressed or revised to better suit our medium. Once in a while, there's been so much good story material in a particular episode, I split it into two or sometimes three issues. "SLAVE ISLAND" collected herein, is one example. And the dialogue is always a challenge. This is, after all, quite the international group of people. On television, there is this wonderful element called sound. People have actual voices you can hear, with accents and inflections that add character depth. Rogue has her sexy Southern dialect; Colossus speaks a very formal English, overlaid with a slight Russian accent; Gambit's de ragin' Cajun from down Louisiana way. I keep a trusty French/English dictionary handy, the better to more authentically add a French phrase or two. Trying to catch his peculiar brand of Cajun-ese has been one of the more difficult parts of the series for me. But toughest of all is mall baby Jubilee's speech patterns. I can't locate her way-cool quips in any dictionary or reference book, you know. So, I have to spend weekends hanging out at suburban shopping malls, eavesdropping on teenagers' conversations, furiously jotting down each priceless contemporary phrase for future regurgitation through the mouth of Jubilation Lee. Ahh, the suffering we do for our art.

Seriously, it's extremely rewarding scrivening X-MEN ADVENTURES. Both Kelly and Bob, familiar with the subtle difficulties of doing adaptations, have been enormously helpful and supportive. As other X-writers could tell you, it's a bit intimidating putting words in the mouths of the most popular characters in comics. But it's comforting to know that any bonehead logic mistakes I'll make (and there have been plenty) will be unfailingly zeroed in on by the great overseer I call editor Kelly Corvese. Kelly, of course, will explain my stupidity to me in such a soothing, parental fashion, I almost don't fear for my continued tenure on this title. Almost.

I'll mention that my favorite X-Man to write is the bouncing, blushing, bluish Beast — Hank McCoy. I love his amazingly erudite words coming from that hairy, animalistic bod. It's playing against type in the Marvel Manner. Unfortunately, Hank wasn't in many of the first season shows, so I've truly treasured the few times he's appeared.

Enough of my ranting. We've collected some of the best of the early X-MEN ADVENTURES here. There's Storm's epic confrontation with Morlock leader Callisto. Sabretooth's savage assault on the old canucklehead, Wolverine. And, we present the first appearance of the mysterious Cable in these pages, too. What more could you want? For me it was both an honor and kick scripting this stuff. And hey, my so far brief association with the X-Men has even gotten me a few seconds of undeserved fame on television's Entertainment Tonight program. What more could I want? Not much. Enjoy.

Ralph Macchio

NIGHT OF THE SENTINELS

"WITNESS THE **DESTRUCTION** CAUSED BY THE AWESOME **SABRETOOTH**. GAZE UPON THE **WRATH** OF THE OUTCAST TURNED AGAINST AN UNSYMPATHETIC SOCIETY.

"LOOK AT THE **RESULT** OF MAN'S **OSTRACISM** AND **HATRED** UNLEASHED! SEE WHAT THIS DISTORTED MIRROR REFLECTS.

RRARR!

"ANOTHER OUTBREAK OF MUTANT VIOLENCE TODAY IN NEW YORK CITY..."

HERE!

SHE'S ONE OF THEM, YOU KNOW. ONE OF THOSE **MUTANTS** -- OUR OWN DAUGHTER -- **JUBILEE**. REMEMBER HOW THE VCR WAS MELTED AFTER SHE USED IT. YOU KNOW WHAT WE HAVE TO DO.

YOU MEAN REGISTER HER WITH THE GOVERNMENT LIKE SHE WAS SOME SORT OF **CRIMINAL**? **NEVER**, MARTIN!

WHAT DO YOU WANT ME TO DO, BREAK THE LAW? IT'S FOR HER OWN GOOD. SHE NEEDS HELP.

YOU'D **NEVER** SUGGEST THIS IF SHE WAS REALLY OUR OWN DAUGHTER... AND NOT ADOPTED.

THOOM

TARGET PINPOINT IMMINENT, DISTANCE TWENTY METERS.

PROCEEDING.

SCANNING.

MUTANT FILE 051063-244

Subject: Jubilee
Name: Jubilation Lee
Height: 5'
Weight: 96 lbs
Race: Chinese-American
Address: 764 Lucille Court West

EXECUTE TARGET ACQUISITION, SUBROUTINE.

MUTANT IDENTIFICATION POSITIVE. TARGET ACQUISITION COMMENCING.

SKRAASSH

WRUNCH

IDENTIFICATION ERROR, NON-MUTANT PILLOW IN CONTOUR OF HUMAN BODY COVERED BY BLANKET. TARGET DESIGNATE: JUBILEE NOT IN QUARTERS.

TARGET'S NEW WHEREABOUTS UNKNOWN, SEARCH RECOMMENCING.

OHMIGOD! WHAT'S HAPPENED?!

JUBILEE! JUBILEE!

HOURS LATER IN NEW YORK'S WESTCHESTER COUNTY...

MMMMM...

HELLO. MY NAME IS ORORO. I AM ALSO CALLED STORM. YOU'RE IN PROFESSOR XAVIER'S SCHOOL FOR GIFTED YOUNGSTERS... HOME OF THE X-MEN.

WE TOOK YOU HERE FROM THE MALL.

RIGHT. MY NAME'S JUBILEE. UMM...AREN'T YOU A LITTLE OLD FOR SCHOOL?

NOT THIS ONE. IT IS WHERE WE LEARN TO CONTROL AND HARNESS OUR MUTANT ABILITIES FOR MANKIND'S BENEFIT.

DO NOT LOOK SHOCKED. WE SUSPECT YOU ARE ONE AS WELL.

Y'MEAN YOU'RE ALL WEIRDOS LIKE ME HERE?

WHO YOU CALLIN' A WEIRDO, SQUIRT?

LOGAN... THIS IS OUR GUEST, JUBILEE. SHE WAS THE YOUNG GIRL MENACED IN THE MALL.

JUBILEE... THIS IS WOLVERINE-- ANOTHER OF THE X-MEN.

W-W-WOLVERINE?

YUP. MINUS THE FIRST TWO W'S.

GOTTA HIT THE WAR ROOM, ORORO. THE PROF'S CHECKIN' OUT MISTER MACHINES' HEAD...

...AN' HE WANTS US ALL PRESENT FOR THE DISSECTION.

I SHALL KEEP HER HOOKED UP TO THE MONITORS IN CASE THERE IS ANY CHANGE IN HER CONDITION.

RELAX, JUBILEE. I WILL RETURN SHORTLY.

STAY BED-RIDDEN, GIRLIE. THE PROF WANTS A WORD WITH YOU LATER.

ME TOO!

I GOTTA MAKE A BREAK FOR IT. I LIKE STORM BUT THAT WOLVERINE DUDE GIVES ME THE CREEPS.

TRSSS

MOM AND DAD MUST BE WORRIED SICK ABOUT ME BY NOW. IF ONLY I WAS NORMAL THEY'D HAVE NO PROBLEMS.

BUT I'M A MUTIE, AND I'LL NEVER BE ANYTHING BUT.

SURE HOPE ANOTHER ONE'A THOSE GIANT THINGS DIDN'T COME AFTER ME AT MY HOUSE.

OH, NUTS-- I WONDER WHAT *GRIEF* MY FOLKS ARE GOING THROUGH RIGHT *NOW*.

I'LL ASK YOU AGAIN, MR. AND MRS. DOBSON, DOES YOUR DAUGHTER HAVE ANY MUTANT FRIENDS? THE FEDERAL GOVERNMENT WANTS TO KNOW.

SHE WAS SEEN ONLY HOURS AGO WITH THESE WOMEN-- BOTH KNOWN MUTANTS.

IF YOU'RE WITHHOLDING INFORMATION, I'LL REMIND YOU IT'S A VERY SERIOUS OFFENSE.

WASHINGTON INTENDS TO KEEP TABS ON MUTANTS... AND I'M AUTHORIZED TO USE *WHATEVER* MEANS NECESSARY TO ENSURE THAT OCCURS.

ARE WE CLEAR ON THAT?

MR. GYRICH, JUBILEE HAS ONLY BEEN OUR DAUGHTER FOR A YEAR. SHE'S A FOSTER CHILD, WE DON'T KNOW HER FRIENDS AT ALL.

WE LOVE HER WITH ALL OUR HEARTS... BUT WE INTEND TO COOPERATE WITH YOU.

GOOD. BY THE WAY, THE GOVERNMENT WILL COMPENSATE YOU FOR THE DAMAGE DONE TO YOUR HOUSE-- EVEN IF YOU HAVE HOMEOWNER'S INSURANCE.

MOMENTS LATER, A BLOCK AWAY...

SNEAKING OUT WASN'T TOO DIFFICULT. GLAD I'M BACK IN NEW SALEM. SEEMS QUIET.

UH-OH! SPOKE TOO SOON! ANOTHER ONE OF THOSE ROBOTS!

YOU BETTER NOT HURT MY PARENTS, YOU CREEP! KEEP AWAY FROM US!

SPLASK

LEAVE ME ALONE!

CAN'T RUN HOME NOW! HAVETA GO THE OTHER WAY WHILE IT'S SCREWED-UP!

TARGET MUTANT APPREHENDED.

PSSS

WHA--?! ANOTHER ONE! AN' MORE GASSSSS!

SLEEP NOW, MY DEAR. AND WHEN YOU AWAKEN, WE'LL HAVE MUCH TO DISCUSS, YOU AND I.

THE X-MEN'S WAR ROOM...

AFTER A CURSORY EXAM I CANNOT YET DETERMINE WHO BUILT THIS MACHINE, AND WHY

ALL ITS SYSTEMS ARE HIGHLY SOPHISTICATED, STATE-OF-THE-ART TECHNOLOGY.

IT OBVIOUSLY TARGETED THE GIRL BECAUSE SHE'S A MUTANT. I SAW HER UNLEASH ENERGY BLASTS FROM HER PALMS AT THE MALL.

DO ANY OF YOU HAVE ANY SUGGESTIONS, THEORIES, ETC.?

IF ONLY YORICK'S MEMORY TAPES COULD BE ACCESSED WE MIGHT--

WE TRIED THAT, HANK. NO GOOD.

X-MEN, AT LEAST A DOZEN MUTANTS HAVE DISAPPEARED IN THE PAST TWO DAYS IN THE NORTH-EASTERN U.S.

ALL HAD REGISTERED WITH THE AGENCY FOR MUTANT AFFAIRS. I'VE PUT THE BUILDING IT'S HOUSED IN ON THE SCREEN.

YOU THINK THE GOVERNMENT IS SECRETLY ROUNDING UP MUTANTS?

NO. THEY'VE ALWAYS BEEN HELPFUL. SOMEONE *INSIDE* THE AGENCY MUST HAVE HIS OWN *HIDDEN* AGENDA.

I'M AFRAID I'M GOING TO ASK YOU TO BREAK INTO THE MUTANT AFFAIRS DEPARTMENT AND *ERASE* THE FILES THEY HAVE ON MUTANTS.

PROFESSOR-- THAT'D BE *BREAKING* THE LAW.

MAYBE YOU DON'T HEAR SO WELL, BUB. *TWELVE* OF OUR OWN *DISAPPEARED* IN FORTY-EIGHT HOURS. THIS *AIN'T* NO CREDIT CARD AGENCY SELLIN' INFO ON US.

IT'S THE *FEDS*. NOW MAYBE YOU NEED SOME *GENTLE PERSUADIN'* TO SEE WHAT'S RIGHT. IF SO...

RETRACT THOSE CLAWS, LOGAN...

...OR LOSE THEM.

TOUGH TALK, CYKE. BUT WE'RE GONNA DO THIS WHETHER YOU'RE LEADIN' THE TROOPS-- OR HERE WRINGIN' YER HANDS PANSY STYLE.

THAT'S ENOUGH. NOW RETIRE TO YOUR QUARTERS UNTIL YOU HEAR FURTHER INSTRUCTIONS.

CYCLOPS, YOU STAY.

SORRY, PROFESSOR. I KNOW I'M DEPUTY LEADER AND I SHOULDN'T CHALLENGE YOUR DECISION, BUT...

THIS DECISION DOESN'T COME EASILY TO ME, SCOTT.

BUT SOMEONE IS USING THE INFORMATION IN THOSE FILES TO *KIDNAP* MUTANTS. WE'VE NEVER FACED A THREAT THIS GRAVE-- AND OUR ENEMY REMAINS UNKNOWN.

I SYMPATHIZE WITH YOUR DOUBTS. BUT I *NEED* YOUR LEADERSHIP MORE THAN EVER.

OF ALL MY X-MEN IT'S *YOU* WHO'VE MADE ME MOST PROUD, SCOTT.

THANK YOU, PROFESSOR.

STORM... AS WE DISCUSSED... COVER.

YES.

I, TOO, SHARE YOUR RESERVATIONS ABOUT OUR MISSION, SCOTT. PERHAPS, IN OUR HEARTS WE FEAR--

"--THE ROLE OF RENEGADES MAY SUIT US MORE THAN WE WISH TO BELIEVE."

THAT'S WHAT I CALL DARKNESS. 'COURSE THERE'S STILL THE MATTER O' THIS FENCE.

THE MEREST OF IMPEDIMENTS, MY HIRSUTE COMPATRIOT.

YEAH. TOO BAD GAMBIT AIN'T DOWN HERE TO GIVE US AN ALLEZ-OOP.

I'M INSIDE. AND NOW THAT I'VE GOTTEN A LOOK AT THE FIRST GUARD...

...IT'S CHILD'S PLAY TO ALTER MY FORM INTO A REPLICA OF HIM.

YOUR LINGUISTIC FLUENCY NEVER FAILS TO IMPRESS, LOGAN.

HEY--COME OVER HERE A MINUTE. LOOK WHAT I'VE FOUND.

HUH?

WHAT'RE YOU DOIN' AWAY FROM-- NO-- IT'S ME-- MY FACE! YOU GOT MY FACE!

AND BOY AM I GONNA BE HAPPY TO GET RID OF IT!

OKAY BOYS--PARTY TIME!

WHOK

HOPEFULLY, OUR FEARSOME SLAVERING VISAGES WILL PRECIPITATE A QUICK SURRENDER OF THE REMAINING DEFENDERS.

BEAST-- SHUT UP AND GET OVER THE FENCE 'FORE I REALLY LOSE IT WITH YOU!

SCOTT-- WHAT'S GOIN' ON IN THEAH?

THEY'RE INSIDE WITHOUT A HITCH, ROGUE.

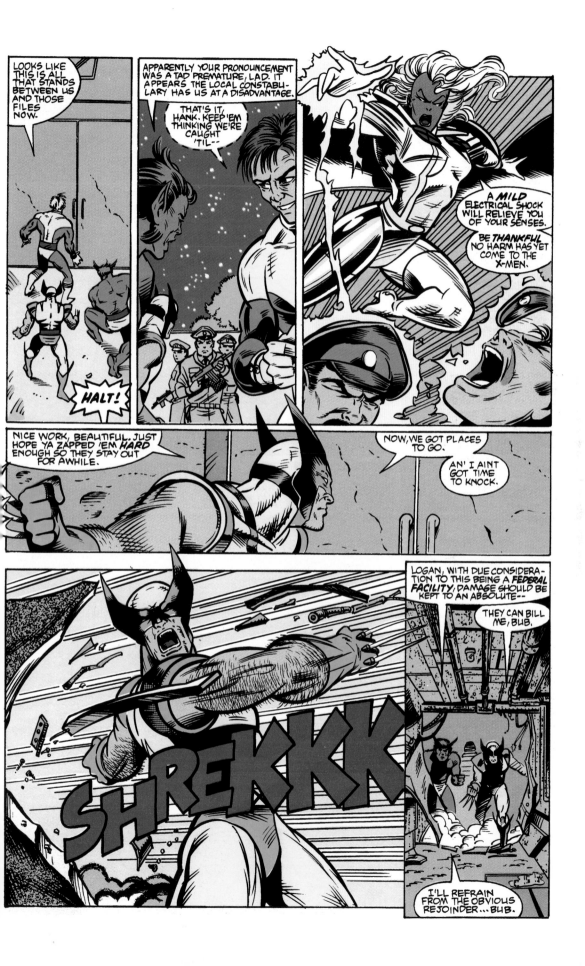

STORM: YOU ARE HESITATING.

WOLVERINE: I CAN SMELL 'EM. OZONE.

CAPTION: ELECTRIC EYE BEAMS.

STORM: AND WE SHALL SEE THEM AS WELL. A BIT OF MIST TO MAKE THEM VISIBLE.

BEAST: ONE SIDE, MADAME, AS THE BLUSHING BEAST ASSUMES CENTER STAGE WHILST ENGAGING IN A REMINISCENCE--

BEAST: --OF THE LATE, LAMENTED *MISSION IMPOSSIBLE* CELLULOID EXTRAVAGANZAS WHEREIN EACH LABORIOUSLY CHOSEN TEAM MEMBER SHOWCASED HIS UNIQUE ABILITIES...

BEAST: ...YET WORKED HARMONIOUSLY TOWARD THE *GROUP* OBJECTIVE, SANS GRANDSTANDING.

BEAST: WOULD THAT SUCH EGREGIOUS DISPLAYS OF TALENT WERE *NOT* A PART OF THIS FURRY FELON'S MAKE-UP, BUT ALAS...

BEAST: AHA, UNLESS I'M SUDDENLY BEREFT OF BRAIN MATTER... THAT BOX-LIKE PROTUBERANCE AHEAD--

BEAST: --CONTAINS THE EYE BEAM *CUT-OFF SWITCHES*, THUS GRANTING OUR UNENCUMBERED AND UNWARRANTED ACCESS--

BEAST: --TO THE FACILITY'S INNARDS.

WOLVERINE: HEY, GOOD WORK, BEAST--B-BUT IT'S GETTIN REAL DARK IN HERE!

WOLVERINE: EVERYBODY'S FADING OUT! I-I CAN'T SEE THEM ANY MORE! WHAT'S GOIN' ON?!

THE X-MANSION WAR ROOM LATER THAT NIGHT.

AND THAT'S ALL THERE IS TO TELL, PROFESSOR. IF I COULD HAVE DONE ANYMORE...

I UNDERSTAND, SCOTT.

WHATTA WHITEWASH! YOU DID *NOTHIN'*, SUMMERS, 'CEPT LEAVE MORPH AND THE BEAST TO *BUY IT!*

I GOT A GOOD MIND TO--

LOGAN! I *KNOW* HOW YOU FEEL, BUT I HAD TO CONSIDER THE SAFETY OF THE *ENTIRE* GROUP.

CYCLOPS IS RIGHT, WOLVERINE. I DIDN'T MAKE HIM DEPUTY LEADER BECAUSE I *DIDN'T* TRUST HIS JUDGMENT.

YER ON MY LIST, CYKE.

PROFESSOR, WHAT DO WE KNOW 'BOUT DOSE WHO OPPOSE US?

SINCE YOU'VE BEEN GONE, JEAN AND I HAVE FORMULATED A PLAN OF ACTION--

--THAT I BELIEVE WILL LEAD TO WHOMEVER IS BEHIND THE MUTANT KIDNAPINGS.

IS THERE ANYTHING WE CAN DO ABOUT THE BEAST, PROFESSOR?

YEAH, AH MISS THE FURRY GUY SOMETHIN' AWFUL AWREADY. WHAT'D YUH SUPPOSE HAPPENED TO HIM?

HE'S BEEN CAPTURED AND DOUBTLESS TAKEN TO A FEDERAL PRISON WHERE HE'LL BE INDICTED FOR FEDERAL OFFENSES.

WHAT CAN DAT BE LIKE FOR SO SENSI-TIVE A SOUL?

I WANTED TO CONGRATULATE YOU AND DOCTOR TRASK ON HOW WELL YOUR SENTINELS PERFORMED.

THANK YOU, COMMANDER.

LET ME *ALSO* INFORM YOU I'M CANCELING THE EXECUTIVE ORDER FOR MUTANT REGISTRATION.

TOP SECRET... EYES ONLY... FILES.

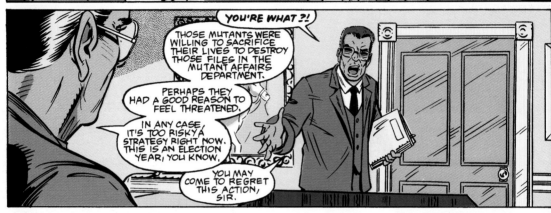

YOU'RE WHAT ?!

THOSE MUTANTS WERE WILLING TO SACRIFICE THEIR LIVES TO DESTROY THOSE FILES IN THE MUTANT AFFAIRS DEPARTMENT.

PERHAPS THEY HAD A GOOD REASON TO FEEL THREATENED.

IN ANY CASE, IT'S TOO RISKY A STRATEGY RIGHT NOW. THIS IS AN ELECTION YEAR, YOU KNOW.

YOU MAY COME TO REGRET THIS ACTION, SIR.

BLAST IT! ALL OF MY MONTHS OF HARD WORK DOWN THE DRAIN BECAUSE THE COMMANDER'S HAVING SECOND THOUGHTS!

MAYBE IT ALL ISN'T LOST. THERE ARE *ALWAYS* ALTERNATIVES.

DOBSON...YOU KNOW WHO THIS IS. WHAT'S THAT? THEY'RE AT YOUR HOME? YOU KNOW WHAT TO DO. I'LL HANDLE THE REST.

YES... YES, MR. GYRICH. I'LL KEEP THEM HERE AS LONG AS I CAN. GOOD-BYE.

THE HOME OF JUBILEE'S FOSTER PARENTS...

SORRY FOR THE INTERRUPTION, MR. SUMMERS. YOU WERE SAYING?

HE THINKS OUR DAUGHTER JUBILEE'S BEEN KIDNAPED BY THOSE THINGS THE COMMANDER TALKED ABOUT.

THOSE SENTINELS.

BUT WHY WOULD THE GOVERNMENT DO SOMETHING LIKE THAT?

BECAUSE PEOPLE FEAR WHAT THEY DON'T UNDERSTAND. IT MAKES THEM DO WRONG THINGS SOMETIMES.

THINGS THEY COME TO REGRET LATER.

I HAVE TO BE GOING NOW. THANK YOU FOR--

MR. SUMMERS, GET OUT OF THIS AREA FAST. SOMEONE'S BEEN IN CONTACT WITH ME, SAID I SHOULD CALL THEM IF ANYBODY CAME ASKING ABOUT JUBILEE.

I-I'M SORRY I WAS-- SCARED. I...

I UNDERSTAND. YOU ONLY WANTED TO HELP YOUR DAUGHTER, AND WE WILL.

UNREGISTERED MUTANT PINPOINTED. TERMINATION PROCEEDING.

WH-WHAT IN THE NAME OF HEAVEN IS THAT?!

PART OF WHAT IT IS YOU FEAR, MR. DOBSON.

I GUESS THIS IS WHERE I BELONG. I'M A "GIFTED YOUNGSTER." AND I CAN BEST LEARN TO USE MY SPECIAL POWER HERE.

BUT IF IT'S SO GOOD FOR ME, HOW COME IT *HURTS* SO MUCH? SO DARN MUCH.

THAT MUST BE JUBILEE, JEAN. SHE'S GOING TO BECOME ONE OF US NOW, AN X-MAN, MAYBE.

I WONDER WHAT THAT POOR GIRL'S BEEN GOING THROUGH. OSTRACIZED BY THE WORLD--LEAVING HER FOSTER PARENTS AFTER ONLY A YEAR.

WHY IS IT ALL SO HARD, SCOTT? WHY WON'T THEY *ACCEPT* US OUT THERE? ALL WE WANT IS TO BE PART OF THE HUMAN RACE... TO FIT IN.

THAT DAY MAY BE A LONG TIME IN COMING, JEAN. UNTIL IT DOES, ALL WE HAVE IS EACH OTHER.

SOMETIMES THAT THOUGHT DOESN'T SEEM SO BAD. IT REALLY DOESN'T.

WE'D BEST GO DOWN AND GREET HER.

ON THIS EARTH, AS ON YOUR OWN, THIS NOBLE BAND OF MUTANTS PERSEVERE DESPITE DIRE CIRCUMSTANCES.

STRENGTH OF CHARACTER IS THEIR BULWARK AGAINST A HARSH HUMANITY. WE SHALL LOOK IN ON THESE WARRIORS AGAIN AND SEE HOW THEY FARE.

THIS I KNOW, FOR I AM THE WATCHER.

NEXT ISSUE: "ENTER MAGNETO!"

E N T E R

MAGNETO

LET THESE GLOWING FRAGMENTS SERVE NOTICE ON THOSE WHO DWELL BELOW...
WHOOM
"...THAT NONE MAY INTERFERE WITH THE MASTER OF MAGNETISM.
"TO THWART MY WILL IS TO INVITE OBLIVION."

THE WESTCHESTER COUNTY MANSION OF PROFESSOR CHARLES XAVIER, LOCATION OF HIS "SCHOOL FOR GIFTED YOUNGSTERS."

EH? A SUDDEN BURST OF LIGHT OUTSIDE.

IT APPEARS TO BE A SHOOTING STAR-- A FRAGMENT OF THE COSMOS COME CALLING ON MOTHER EARTH.

WHAT WAS IT THAT DIVERTED YOU FROM YOUR ENDLESS FLIGHT, I WONDER, TO SKIRT GRAYMALKIN LANE BEFORE IMPACT? SIMPLE GRAVITY, OR--

A PENNY FOR YOUR THOUGHTS, PROFESSOR?

ONE DAY YOU'LL SCAN THEM FOR FREE, SHOULD YOUR POWERS CONTINUE TO DEVELOP.

WHAT MAY I DO FOR YOU THIS EVENING...

YOU REMIND ME OF ANOTHER MUTANT I KNEW LONG AGO. A GREAT MAN... ALSO A FOOL.

BEWARE THE CHOICE YOU HAVE MADE THIS DAY, BEAST. YOU HAVE CHOSEN A PATH THAT WILL LEAD TO YOUR INEVITABLE EXTINCTION.

WORDS UTTERED BY A MADMAN, I WONDER...

...OR A PROPHET?

A WEEK PASSES IN REFLECTION, THEN...

MR. McCOY, THIS IS A BAIL HEARING TO DETERMINE WHAT-- IF AT ALL-- YOUR BAIL SHOULD BE SET AT, PENDING INDICTMENT.

DO YOU HAVE ANY QUESTIONS IN THAT REGARD?

NO, YOUR HONOR.

THEN WE'LL HEAR FROM YOUR DEFENSE LAWYER, MR. HODGE.

YOUR HONOR, MY CLIENT IS CHARGED WITH A SIMPLE FELONY. DENIAL OF BAIL WOULD BE CRUEL AND UNUSUAL.

HOW D'YA LIKE YER HANDIWORK, CYKE? YA LIKE SEEIN' HIM THIS WAY?

SSSH. THIS ISN'T THE TIME, LOGAN. WE'RE HERE TO OBSERVE.

IT WOULD BE MORE A REFLECTION OF HIS MUTANT STATUS THAN THAT OF HIS ALLEGED CRIME.

NOW, MR. HODGE, YOU KNOW THIS COURT HARBORS NO PREJUDICE. ANY INSINUATION TO THE CONTRARY WILL NOT BE TOLERATED.

YOUR HONOR, AS A REPRESENTAIVE OF THE PEOPLE, I MUST SPEAK.

THIS... MAN IS ALLEGED TO HAVE TAKEN PART IN THE BREAK-IN AT A FEDERAL FACILITY.

HE ACTED *VIOLENTLY* WHEN ATTEMPTS AT APPREHENSION WERE MADE. THIS MAN BELONGS BEHIND BARS--

--*NOT* OUT AMONGST DECENT FOLKS.

A BRIEF BUT COMPELLING CASE HAS JUST BEEN MADE FOR BAIL DENIAL, MR. HODGE. RESPONSE?

YOUR HONOR, WITH RESPECT--THIS IS A BAIL HEARING, NOT A TRIAL. MY CLIENT REACTED AS ANYONE WOULD UNDER SUCH FRIGHTENING CIRCUMSTANCES.

HOW SO?

HE STRUCK BACK IN SELF-DEFENSE AS HE'S HAD TO DO HIS ENTIRE LIFE AGAINST A WORLD THAT'S BEEN HOSTILE TO HIM AND HIS KIND.

LET US NOT FORGET THE DISAPPEARANCE OF ELEVEN MUTANTS--ALL RECENT REGISTRANTS WITH THE DEPARTMENT OF MUTANT AFFAIRS.

YOUR HONOR, THIS IS RIDICULOUS. MR. HODGE IS ATTEMPTING TO *JUSTIFY* HIS CLIENT'S CRIMINAL ACTIONS WITH A SLANDEROUS *ATTACK* ON A PROGRAM DESIGNED TO HELP MUTANTS.

YOUR CONCERN IS NOTED, MR. PROSECUTOR.

I THINK AT THIS TIME WE'LL HEAR FROM MR. McCOY HIMSELF, AND ALLOW HIM TO STATE WHY HE BELIEVES BAIL SHOULD BE GRANTED.

THANK YOU, SIR.

MR. HODGE HAS DONE A FINE JOB OF REPRESENTING ME, BUT WHAT CAN ANY HUMAN TRULY KNOW OF A MUTANT'S EXISTENCE-- THE PAIN AND TORMENT.

THE X-MANSION'S WAR ROOM...

ACCORDING TO THE NEWS REPORTS, ANOTHER MUTANT ATTEMPTED TO BREAK HANK OUT OF THE DETENTION CENTER.

APPARENTLY, HANK REMAINED WHILE THE OTHER ONE FLED.

I'VE CONFIRMED THE IDENTITY OF THE BEAST'S WOULD-BE RESCUER. IT'S AN OLD FRIEND.

AN OLD FRIEND? WHO PROFESSOR?

OUR PATHS HAVE CROSSED MANY TIMES, HE WAS A MAN I ONCE KNEW AS *MAGNUS*. NOW, HE CALLS HIMSELF-- *MAGNETO*.

NUTS! WE SHOULD'A BEEN THERE, PROFESSOR. I WOULD'A DRIVEN THE GETAWAY CAR!

NICE TO SEE ONE O' US WITH SOME *SPUNK*, AIN'T IT, SUMMERS?

THAT'S UNCALLED FOR, WOLVERINE,

I HOPED NEVER TO SEE HIS LIKE AGAIN.

OUR VIEWS ON THE MUTANT'S PLACE IN THIS WORLD ARE SO DIVERGENT AS TO BE IRRECONCILABLE, HE BELIEVES OUR DESTINY IS TO TREAD MANKIND BENEATH OUR FEET.

HOMO SAPIENS SUPERIOR IS TO *DOMINATE* HUMANITY-- NOT TO LIVE IN HARMONY WITH IT. I'VE SPENT MY LIFE IN CONFLICT WITH SUCH A REPELLENT VIEW.

CLANDESTINELY, IN THE PAST, MAGNUS HAS ATTACKED POWER STATIONS DEFENSE FACTORIES, *ET CETERA*, IN THE TWISTED HOPE HE COULD CAUSE *CIVIL WAR* BETWEEN MAN AND MUTANT. HE FAILED.

NOW HE HAS RETURNED, APPARENTLY MORE BRAZEN THAN BEFORE, AND OUR TASK IS TO USE *EVERY* RESOURCE AVAILABLE TO SEE TO MAGNUS'S *DEFEAT*.

HE'S TOAST.

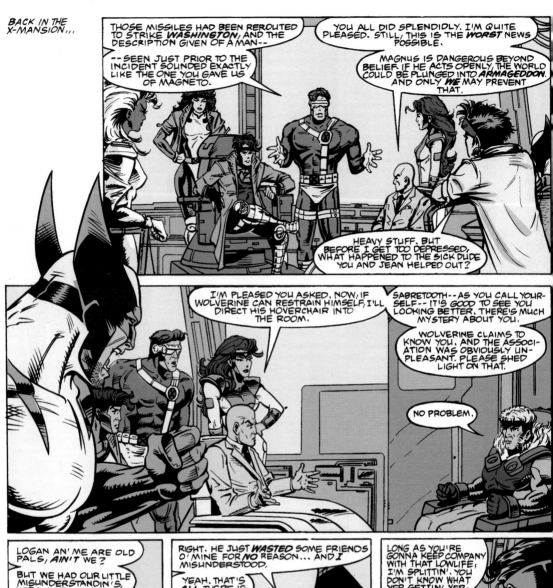

THOSE MISSILES HAD BEEN REROUTED TO STRIKE *WASHINGTON*, AND THE DESCRIPTION GIVEN OF A MAN--

-- SEEN JUST PRIOR TO THE INCIDENT SOUNDED EXACTLY LIKE THE ONE YOU GAVE US OF MAGNETO.

YOU ALL DID SPLENDIDLY. I'M QUITE PLEASED. STILL, THIS IS THE *WORST* NEWS POSSIBLE.

MAGNUS IS DANGEROUS BEYOND BELIEF. IF HE ACTS OPENLY, THE WORLD COULD BE PLUNGED INTO *ARMAGEDDON*. AND ONLY *WE* MAY PREVENT THAT.

HEAVY STUFF. BUT BEFORE I GET TOO DEPRESSED, WHAT HAPPENED TO THE SICK DUDE YOU AND JEAN HELPED OUT?

I'M PLEASED YOU ASKED. NOW, IF WOLVERINE CAN RESTRAIN HIMSELF, I'LL DIRECT HIS HOVERCHAIR INTO THE ROOM.

SABRETOOTH-- AS YOU CALL YOUR-SELF-- IT'S GOOD TO SEE YOU LOOKING BETTER. THERE'S MUCH MYSTERY ABOUT YOU.

WOLVERINE CLAIMS TO KNOW YOU, AND THE ASSOCI-ATION WAS OBVIOUSLY UN-PLEASANT. PLEASE SHED LIGHT ON THAT.

NO PROBLEM.

LOGAN AN' ME ARE OLD PALS, *AIN'T* WE?

BUT WE HAD OUR LITTLE MISUNDERSTANDIN'S, NOTHIN' BIG, MIND YA.

RIGHT. HE JUST *WASTED* SOME FRIENDS O' MINE FOR *NO* REASON... AND *I* MISUNDERSTOOD.

YEAH, THAT'S *ALL* THERE IS TO IT, YOU CREEP!

WATCH THE THREADS.

LONG AS YOU'RE GONNA KEEP COMPANY WITH THAT LOWLIFE, I'M SPLITTIN'. YOU DON'T KNOW WHAT YER GETTIN' YER-SELVES INTO.

LOGAN. COME BACK.

STOW IT, CYKE.

ALL THAT IS METALLIC ON THIS PLANET, FROM ELEMENT TO ALLOY, IS UNDER MY CONTROL.

WITH SUCH POWER AS THIS, WHAT GOAL IS BEYOND MY GAZE-- WHAT ENEMY IS BEYOND MY REACH?

MASTER OF *CHAOS!* MASTER OF *MAGNETISM!* AND MASTER OF THE COMING AGE OF *HOMO SAPIENS SUPERIOR!*

ALL THIS AM I!

WHERE IS THE FORCE ON THIS PITIFUL GLOBE WHICH CAN OPPOSE ME? *WHERE* ARE THOSE WHO WILL CHALLENGE ME?

EH?

PLINK

JUST LOOK OVAH YOAH LIL OL' SHOULDER, SHUGAH!

YOUR MUTANT ABILITY IS TO CHANNEL INTENSE BEAMS OF LIGHT THROUGH YOUR EYES.

POTENTIALLY DEVASTATING--SAVE THAT A MAGNETICALLY-INDUCED FORCE FIELD RENDERS IT USELESS.

--AND WE'RE TAKING YOU *DOWN!*

I AWAIT YOUR NEXT MODE OF ATTACK. SURELY, CHARLES HAS TAUGHT YOU ALTERNATIVE STRATEGIES.

SCOTT! WHAT'D THAT BULLET-HEADED BOZO DO TO YUH?

GAS FROM ≶COUGH≶ VAT--CAN'T BREATHE--GOING UNDER! DON'T ≶COUGH≶ ≶COUGH≶ WORRY ABOUT ME!

GAS CLOUDS SWIRLING AROUND ME FROM ONE OF THE SMASHED VATS. FEELING DIZZY...

KEEP UP THE ≶GASP≶ ATTACK, ROGUE! GET ≶COUGH≶ ON HIM!

BAH! A FRONTAL ASSAULT AGAINST SUCH A SUPERIOR ADVERSARY? ARE YOU BEREFT OF YOUR SENSES? IT IS *SINFUL* THAT SUCH AS YOU ARE OF MY BREED!

BNAM

UNMPH GOTTA GET BACK ON MUH FEET—CAN'T LET THAT SCOUNDREL JUST FLY OFF WITHOUT ME GETTIN' A SHOT IN!

AH GOT MORE STRENGTH THAN AH KNOW WHAT TO DO WITH... AND AH NEED IT ALL NOW! MPMH C'MON, GIRL—PUSH!

STORM! LEMME SEE YUH BREATHIN', GAL. IT'S GONNA BE OKAY—JUST ROUSE YUHSELF ...C'MON, AH'M GONNA HELP YUH!

HEY, YUH LOOK SHAKY ON YUH PINS, ORORO. LEASTWISE—YOU'RE ALIVE!

WE GOT OUR CLOCKS CLEANED BUT GOOD, LADY. BUT WE AIN'T LETTIN' HIM SLIP TOWN, ARE WE?

NO.

NO. WE ARE NOT. WE ARE X-MEN.

HOW IS CYCLOPS FARING?

AH'M GONNA GIVE HIM MOUTH-TO-MOUTH 'CAUSE THOSE TOXIC FUMES DID A JOB ON HIM.

'COURSE I AIN'T SURE WHAT'LL HAPPEN AFTER AH TOUCH HIM 'CAUSE YUH KNOW AH ABSORB THE POWER'A ANYBODY I'M IN CONTACT WITH—

—EVEN IF AH DON'T WANT IT TO HAPPEN.

DON'T DIE ON ME, SCOTTIE BOY. AH' COULDN'T TAKE IT IF I HAD TO FACE THE PROFESSOR—

—AND TELL HIM HIS SHININ' BOY DIDN'T MAKE IT.

DON'T DIE.

THE CAPITOL BUILDING, WASHINGTON D.C.,...

THANK YOU FOR ASSEMBLING, LADIES AND GENTLEMEN OF THE PRESS. I'LL KEEP MY REMARKS BRIEF.

SINCE OUR COUNTRY'S LEADERS *RECKLESSLY* RESCINDED THE MUTANT REGISTRATION ACT, THE MUTANT CRIMINAL ELEMENT HAS RUN *WILD*.

THE RECENT MUTANT ATTACKS AT THE FLEMINGTON MISSILE BASE AND THE METRO CHEMICAL PLANT ARE *JUST* THE BEGINNING.

SENATOR KELLY, WHAT DO YOU PLAN TO DO ABOUT THIS?

I INTEND, IN THIS CHAMBER, TONIGHT, TO DECLARE MY *CANDIDACY* FOR THE PRESIDENCY OF THE UNITED STATES.

IT'S OBVIOUS THE CURRENT ADMINISTRATION HAS GIVEN THE GREEN LIGHT TO MUTANT LAW-BREAKING.

AS PRESIDENT, I INTEND TO PLACE *EVERY* MUTANT IN THE NATION IN SPECIALLY-DESIGNED INTERNMENT CAMPS UNDER *MILITARY* SUPERVISION.

I WILL USE THIS ISSUE AS MY BASIS FOR RUNNING FOR THIS NATION'S HIGHEST OFFICE.

YOU'RE THE PERFECT TOOL, KELLY. GLIB AND FACILE WITH WORDS. JUST WHAT PETER GYRICH* NEEDS IN THE COMING MONTHS.

* THE FED IN CHARGE OF THE NOW DISBANDED REGISTRATION PROGRAM, WHO TOOK HIS JOB A WEE TOO *SERIOUS*. --Inside-the-Beltway Kel.

MAKE ME *PUKE*, SENATOR *SLIMEBALL!* I WOULDN'T VOTE FOR THAT *DWEEB* IF HE RAN AGAINST PEE-WEE HERMAN.

RRRRGH! JUST LEMME GET MY *CLAWS* ON HIS *THROAT* AN' HE WON'T BE MAKIN' ANY MORE FANCY SPEECHES.

S-SORRY, KID. STILL TOUGH FOR ME TO CONTROL MY ANGER. BUT THE PROF'S TREATMENTS ARE WORKIN'. IT'S GETTIN' EASIER.

GREAT. AND I'M THE ONE'S GOTTA STAY HERE AND WATCH YOU, LAME-O.

WHERE ARE YOU FROM? YOU SHOWED UP HERE BLEEDING AND HALF-DEAD.

...SAID YOU WERE A *KILLER* AND OTHER STUFF SO YOU GOTTA STAY *STRAPPED* IN THAT HOVERCHAIR WHILE YOU GET TREATED.

THEN THE PROF TOOK YOU IN AND TRIED TO HELP YOU. THAT MADE WOLVERINE FLIP OUT...

AN' HOW MUCH MORE YA KNOW ABOUT WOLVERINE THAN ME, HUH? HE'S GOT A *TEMPER* MAKES ME LOOK LIKE A BOY SCOUT!

SO HOW COME *ME* AIN'T STRAPPED IN HERE GETTIN' SOME SPECIAL TREATMENT TO HELP CHANGE HIM?

WELL, YOU GOT A POINT THERE. HE IS KINDA *CREEPY.* AN--

--OH, LOOK, YOUR WRIST'S BLEEDING FROM THE RESTRAINTS. CAN'T LET IT GET INFECTED.

PROMISE YOU'LL STAY CALM WHILE I TRY TO BANDAGE IT.

NO SWEAT. I BEEN STUCK IN THIS FLYIN' ROCKIN' CHAIR SO LONG I CAN BARELY MOVE A MUSCLE, ANYWAY.

OKAY. HERE GOES. JUST THE WRIST THINGY, REMEMBER.

AHH. THAT'S BETTER. MUCH, MUCH BETTER!

THE END...

X-MEN ADVENTURES

CAPTIVE HEARTS

SLAVE ISLAND

RALPH MACCHIO
writer

ANDREW WILDMAN
CHRIS BATISTA
pencilers

ROBERT CAMPANELLA
ANDREW PEPOY
MARK McKENNA
inkers

MICHAEL HIGGINS
letterer

DANA MORESHEAD
ARIANE
colorists

KELLY CORVESE
editor

BOB HARRAS
group editor

TOM DeFALCO
editor in chief

based on the teleplays by
ROBERT N. SKIR
MARTY ISENBERG
MICHAEL EDENS

CAPTIVE HEARTS

SO DO I, *PETITE.* STILL, I AM *GRATEFUL* FOR DE ASSIST--EMBARRASSING AS IT MAY BE.

JUBILEE'S EXPRESSION INDICATES SHE IS BEGINNING TO UNDERSTAND THE SERIOUSNESS OF THESE SESSIONS.

THE X-MEN'S COUNTERATTACK STRATEGIES AND REFLEXES MUST BE HONED TO PERFECTION. THAT CAN ONLY OCCUR IF THE THREAT IS *REAL.*

BUT IT IS THE LEADERSHIP QUALITIES OF *STORM* I AM MOST CONCERNED WITH THIS TIME.

CEILING-MOUNTED CANNONS! I WILL DEAL WITH THIS THREAT--

--BY *FREEZING* AS MANY OF THEM AS POSSIBLE WITH ARCTIC TEMPERATURE WIND.

FRZZZZT

BUT THERE ARE *MORE* THAN I CAN HANDLE SINGLY.

ELSEWHERE IN THE X-MANSION, WOLVERINE ATTEMPTS TO RECOVER FROM BATTLE-WOUNDS AS JEAN GREY OBSERVES.

HA!!

WOLVERINE! YOU'RE SUPPOSED TO BE RESTING! SABRETOOTH NEARLY KILLED YOU.* EVEN WITH YOUR HEALING FACTOR...

I'LL MAKE IT, RED.

*IN X-MEN ADVENTURES TRADE PAPERBACK VOL.#1 --Kelly

NEVER SHOULD'A LET--UNH--MY GUARD DOWN. DESERVE THIS.

DON'T TALK LIKE THAT, LOGAN. YOU SAVED JUBILEE'S LIFE. THAT WAS WONDERFUL-- HEROIC.

YEAH--I'M A REGULAR ERROL FLYNN.

DON'T LOOK AT ME THAT WAY, LADY. YER EYES ARE SAYIN' WE BEEN THINKIN' ABOUT THE SAME THING, AIN'T WE?

HAVE TO SEE SCOTT. MUST GO.

THAT EVENING, ALONG MANHATTAN'S BROADWAY...

OH, SCOTT, GETTING AWAY FROM THE MANSION AND ALL THE PRESSURES THERE-- COMING TO THE CITY-- I LOVE IT.

YEAH... ME, TOO, JEAN.

IF ONLY FOR THE GOOD OF THE TEAM, THE DEPUTY LEADER NEEDS TO RELAX ONCE IN AWHILE. I KNOW I CAN GET INTENSE...

...BUT THE THREATS WE FACE, THE--

SCOTT, WE'RE OFF TONIGHT.

SORRY. I-- WAIT-- WHAT'S THIS?

WE *CAN'T* ESCAPE IT. EVERYWHERE WE GO-- REMINDERS OF WHAT KIND OF *MONSTERS* WE'RE SEEN AS!

TIMES

MUTANT MADNESS

TELEGRAPH

MUTANT MENACE

WE LEAD THESE DOUBLE LIVES TO SAFE-GUARD HUMANI-TY AND THIS IS OUR THANKS.

LIGHTEN UP. WE *DID* BREAK INTO A FEDERAL FACILITY, AFTER ALL.✱ I *KNOW* WE HAD A GOOD REASON, BUT...

✱ SEE X.A.T.B. VOL. #1 AGAIN.--Kelly

YOU'RE RIGHT, JEAN. Y'KNOW, YOU'RE A GOOD FRIEND AND I NEED TO BE WITH YOU-- AWAY FROM THE OTHERS.

SCOTT, LOOK OVER THERE. SOME STRANGE-LOOKING LITTLE MAN IS LEVITATING FRUIT.

LEGGO MY GOODS, FREAK! YOU MUST BE ONE'A THEM *MUTANTS!*

SURE HOPE THE LOVE-BIRDS ARE HAVIN' THEM-SELVES A TIME DOWN IN THE BIG, BAD CITY.

MAYBE THEY'LL GET *MUGGED!*

THE TUNNELS BELOW MANHATTAN...

UMMMPH, TOO BAD WE DON'T HAVE A DANGER ROOM SEQUENCE THAT DEALS WITH CROWD CONTROL.

SN**IKT**

M-MY GLASSES--*GONE!* BUT MY *EYES*--NOT SHOOTING OPTIC BLASTS! HOW--?!

YOU HELP LEECH-- HE HELPS YOU, LEECH ABSORB YOUR POWER FOR AWHILE. IT COME BACK.

WE GO NOW,

GO?

JUST A MINUTE! I'M NOT GOING *ANYWHERE!* WHAT THE *BLAZES* IS GOING ON HERE?!

YOU WILL FIND OUT ALL YOU WISH. NOW KEEP SILENT.

IF I DIDN'T FEEL SO WEAK...

HE IS HERE--AS YOU ORDERED, MISTRESS.

UNGH!

THIS BLINKING DOT IS AS CLOSE AS I CAN LOCATE THEM AFTER MY BRIEF CONTACT WITH JEAN.

YOU ARE TO HEAD FOR MANHATTAN IMMEDIATELY.

AN' *I'M* GOIN' FOR THE RIDE, TOO, CHARLIE. GOT MY STRENGTH BACK.

STORM, I WANT YOU TO LEAD THE GROUP.

YES, ORORO, *YOU.* IN THE ABSENCE OF THE DEPUTY LEADER, YOU ARE THE BEST QUALIFIED-- DESPITE YOUR OWN RESERVATIONS.

WE ARE AT YOUR DISPOSAL, CHERIE... AND *PROUD* TO BE SO, NO?

THANK YOU, GAMBIT.

A HALF HOUR LATER, BENEATH NEW YORK'S STREETS...

HOW YOU DOIN' HEAH, STORM.

I WILL HANDLE IT, ROGUE.

WOLVERINE, ARE YOU CERTAIN THAT--

I GOT THE SCENT, LEADER-LADY, DON'T WORRY.

WE GOT A WELCOMIN' COMMITTEE.

ON YER TOES.

ARRR!

WE HAVE LITTLE TIME TO WASTE ON THEM.

THE PAIN WRACKED FIGURE COLLAPSES INTO UNCONSCIOUSNESS AS HIS MUTANT METABOLISM CLOSES THE WOUNDS, MIRACULOUSLY RESTORING THE TISSUE TO ITS NORMAL HEALTH AND VIGOR.

THE SNARLS OF HIS CHEATED ENEMY GROW DISTANT-- REPLACED BY THE SOUND OF LAPPING WAVES AGAINST THE ICE FLOE THAT BEARS HIM AWAY.

''' FAR AWAY, UNTIL--

--DISCOVERY.

HE'S *ALIVE.*

UNNNNN...

NO TELLING HOW LONG HE HAS SUFFERED EXPOSURE. WE MUST TAKE HIM TO THE VILLAGE, *KEUWOCK.*

POOYETAH, THE STRANGER COULD BRING A *BIG* REWARD IF WE TAKE HIM SOUTH TO THE GOVERNMENT SETTLEMENT.

MAYBE ENOUGH FOR A NEW SNOWMOBILE.

MOMENTS LATER...

ALL THE PEOPLE ARE MISSIN', BUT I GOT A HUNCH--'CAUSE EVEN WITH ALL THE SMOKE-- THERE'S NO WAY I'M GETTIN' THIS SCENT WRONG!

SABRETOOTH!

BET HE RAN INTO YOU SOMEWHERE AN' YOU TWO HAD A LITTLE POW WOW, HUH?

YES. IT IS TRUE.

YOU MADE THE OTHER TRIBESMEN LAUGH AT ME. YOU STOLE MY POSITION. BEFORE YOU CAME-- I WAS LOOKED UP TO AND ADMIRED.

I WANTED **REVENGE.** THE OTHER STRANGER SAID TO LEAD YOU AWAY FROM THE CAMP AND HE WOULD SET A TRAP. BUT I BECAME OVER-ANXIOUS. SCARED.

BUT **THIS**... I-I DIDN'T KNOW ABOUT THIS. BELIEVE ME.

I BELIEVE YA. I BELIEVE YER A STUPID, GLORY-GRABBIN' **PUNK** WHO DON'T KNOW WHEN HE'S GOT IT GOOD!

WELL, HOW'D YA **LIKE** THE RESULTS A YER LITTLE SCHEME? YOU BEEN PLAYED FER A **SAP**-- AN' EVERYONE YA KNOWS **PAYIN'** FER IT.

NOW, I'M FOLLOWIN' THESE TRACKS NO MATTER WHERE THEY LEAD--

--CAUSE I GOT A **SCORE** TO SETTLE WITH SABRETOOTH!

YOU WANNA TAG ALONG --YER WELCOME, MAYBE YOU'LL BE A HERO.

BUT I GOTTA WARN YA... WHAT'S COMIN' UP AIN'T GONNA BE PRETTY.

YOU STILL GAME, KELUWOCK?

I WILL COME WITH YOU, WOLVERINE. THERE IS NOTHING FOR ME HERE NOW.

THAT SETTLES IT 'TWEEN US. NOW I GOTTA GET THOSE ESKIMOS OUTTA HERE!

HOPE THE KID DID HIS PART AND UNSHACKLED 'EM BE-FOR HE-- YEP!

DON'T STAND THERE *LOOKIN'* AT ME, MAN!

CLEAR OUT-- 'CAUSE THIS DEVICE IS DETONATIN' IN ABOUT FIVE SECONDS--

BWOOM

--OR LESS!

EXPLOSION'S ROCKIN' THE WHOLE GLACIER! THIS PART'S LETTIN' LOOSE *NOW!*

EDGE-- SLIPPERY! LOSIN' MY GRIP! GOTTA PULL MYSELF UP OR IT'S OVER!

SKRMMM

HERE, FRIEND WOLVERINE. TAKE MY HAND. THERE WILL BE NO MORE LOSS OF LIFE THIS DAY.

SEEMS LIKE THERE'S BEEN ENOUGH TO LAST A LIFETIME.

YOU MEAN KELIWOCK, THE HEADSTRONG ONE.

YER BOY, YEAH. NOTHIN' I CAN SAY...

...'CEPT THAT HE WENT OUT A HERO. YER WHOLE TRIBE CAN BE PROUD. I AM.

LATER, AT THE BURNT VILLAGE... A SMALL FUNERAL.

EVERYBODY'S GOT THEIR RITUALS, POOYETAH. BUT DEATH'S **STILL** DEATH.

YES, AND LIFE **MUST** CONTINUE. UNTIL OUR DWELLINGS ARE REPLACED, WE WILL HAVE TO MOVE TO THE GOVERNMENT SETTLE-MENT FOR AWHILE.

STILL, WE HAVE EACH OTHER. WHAT DO **YOU** HAVE, WOLVERINE?

I WALKED OUT ON THE ONLY FAMILY I KNEW, SITUATION THERE GOT TO BE TOO MUCH TO DEAL WITH,

SO I SPLIT FER THE FAR NORTH TO-- I DUNNO-- DEAL WITH MY FEELIN'S.

AND 'CAUSE OF IT, KELIWOK'S--

GO BACK TO THEM, I AM SURE THOSE YOU LEFT WILL EMBRACE YOU AGAIN.

AND IF NOT, YOU HAVE BUT TO SEEK US OUT. YOU HAVE A PLACE HERE-- ALWAYS.

'PRECIATE IT. SOMETIMES EVEN A LONER'S GOTTA KNOW SOMEBODY'S BURNIN' A CANDLE IN THE WINDOW FER 'IM SOMEWHERE.

MAYBE I'LL BE SEEIN' YOU AGAIN, MISTER. TAKE CARE.

SLAVE ISLAND

LET ME FREE!

AT THE UNFINISHED DAM....

OHMIGOD! I CAN'T IMAGINE WHAT IT'S LIKE FOR HER TO BE IN THAT PUNISH-MENT BOX!

STORM'S *CLAUSTROPHOBIC!* SHE MUST BE GOIN' NUTS!

SHE IS ALIVE, PETITE. MORE WE CANNOT ASK AT DIS--

--WHAT--EXPLOSIONS!

YOW! WHAT'S UP WITH THAT?!

MR. TRASK, IT'S HIM.

QUIET! I KNOW.

YEAH.... YOU FEEBS KEEP LOOKIN' THE OTHER WAY WHILE I PLASMA BLAST A LITTLE WIRE--

--THAT'S GONNA COME IN VEEEEERY HANDY.

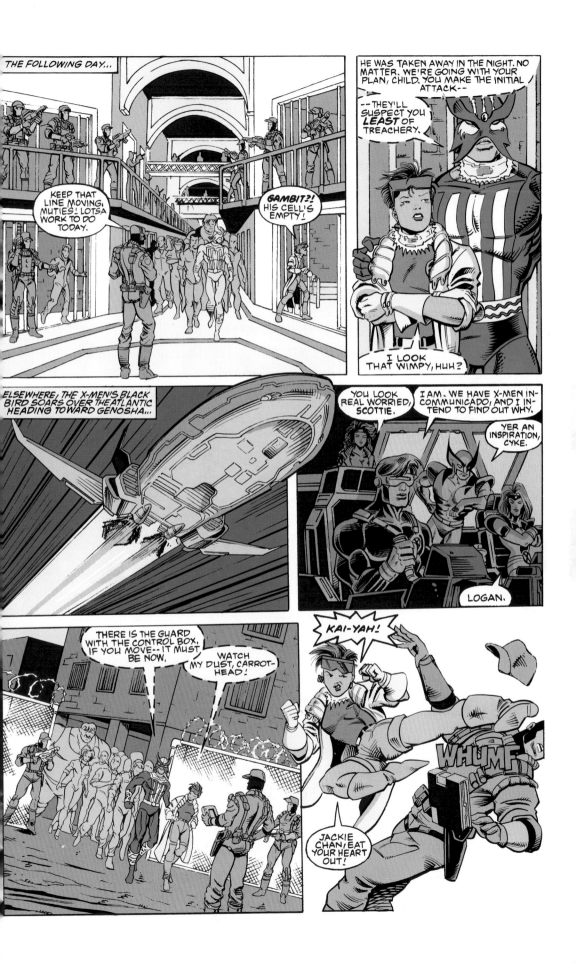

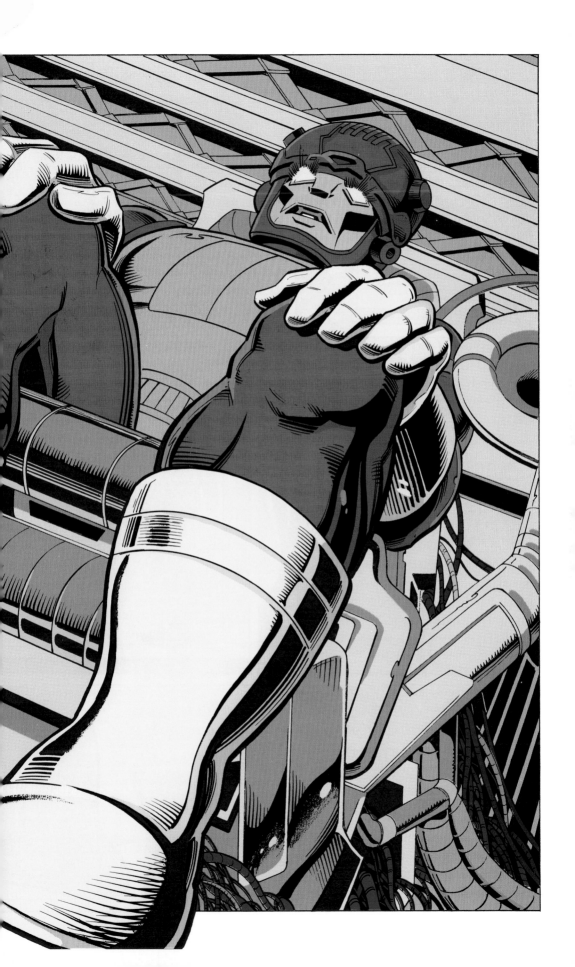

THRMMMMMM

"EXACTLY. THINK OF IT AS A GIANT ALL-PURPOSE OVEN THAT BAKES A SENTINEL-- GOING FROM DOUGH-LIKE TEXTURE TO METALLIC HARDNESS..."

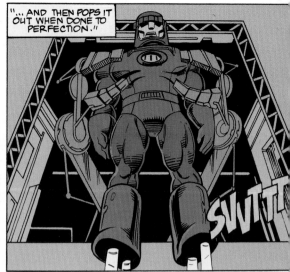

"...AND THEN POPS IT OUT WHEN DONE TO PERFECTION."

SVTTT

MAGNIFICENT AND ACCOMPLISHED USING THE RESOURCES OF THIS BACKWARD ISLAND.

I'M NOT SURE THE LEADER WOULD LIKE HIS COUNTRY REFERRED TO AS "BACKWARD," GYRICH.

I'LL ALLOW MR. GYRICH HIS SLICE OF INNATE YANKEE CONDESCENSION. IT HAS ITS CHARM.

DON'T YOU AGREE, MR. HODGE?*

AS YOUR DEVELOPMENT ADVISOR, COLONEL, I'D PREFER NOT TO COMMENT ON MATTERS OF COMMON COURTESY.

GREETINGS, DR. TRASK. I UNDERSTAND THERE WAS A REVOLT BY THE SLAVES WHICH YOU *ALLOWED* TO OCCUR.

OBVIOUSLY DONE TO BREAK THEIR SPIRIT AND DISCOURAGE FURTHER ATTEMPTS AT SEDITION.

EVERYONE'S GOT TO LEARN THEIR PLACE, HODGE.

"WHEN WE'VE COMPLETED ENOUGH OF THESE, WE MAY NOT NEED YOUR DIRECTIONS TO LOCATE YOUR X-PATRIATES..."

...IF YOU'LL PARDON MY WITTICISM. AND NOW THAT YOUR CURRENT USEFULNESS IS AT AN END, YOU'LL BE RETURNED TO THE PRISON UNTIL WE HAVE NEED OF YOU.

BUT I--

BUT NOTHING! GUARDS, REMOVE THIS JUDAS.

WHAT'S IT LIKE TO BE A STINKING MUTIE -- TO KNOW THE WHOLE WORLD HATES YOUR GUTS?

AW, DON'T ASK 'IM TOUGH QUESTIONS LIKE THAT. YOU KNOW THEIR KIND'S A LITTLE DENSE UPSTAIRS.

AHHH, GOOD TO KNOW DAT ALL REMY THOUGHT 'BOUT HUMANS IS TRUE.

IN DE FACE OF YOUR PROBING QUESTIONS, DIS BOY FROM DE BAYOU GOTTA RESPOND BY SAYIN'--

--VA TE FAIRE FUTRE!

OH, BOY! I T'INK I BEEN DISSED IN FRENCH!

ONLY DE FINEST FOR YOU, HOMMES.

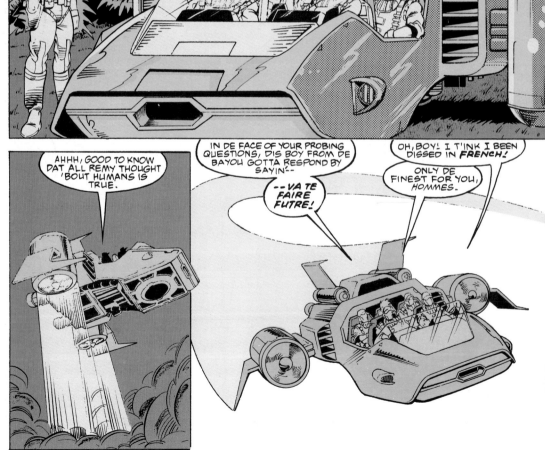

M'SIEURS... ALLOW ME TO SHORTEN DE JOURNEY WITH DE CARD TRICKS, S'IL VOUS PLAIT?

MERCI.

KEEP DE EYES ON DIS DECK AND SEE WHAT DISAPPEARS AS YOU WATCH.

SOME TRICK. NOTHING'S HAPPENING.

FLIKK

AU CONTRAIRE! YOU--MES AMIS--BE-COME LES PLOUCS!

SNOK

BWAK

AND OL' REMY-- HE BECOME SCARCE! AU REVOIR!

"WHO IS THIS MAN--THE ONE YOU'RE SO AFRAID OF, COLONEL?"

"I'D ADVISE DISCRETION IN YOUR WORDS, MR. GYRICH. REMEMBER, YOU AND TRASK CAME TO GENOSHA BECAUSE YOUR PRESIDENT HAD SHUT DOWN YOUR BELOVED SENTINEL MUTANT-HUNTING PROGRAM.

"I WELCOMED YOU HERE BECAUSE ANY SYSTEM THAT WOULD PROMOTE THE IN-CARCERATION OF MUTANTS IS A GOOD ONE. THAT'S WHAT GENOSHA'S ALL ABOUT."

BUT I DID **NOT** PROMISE SMOOTH SAILING. THIS MAN **CABLE**--AN AMERICAN APPARENTLY. WE SUSPECT HE'S A MUTANT.

HE WAS A MERCENARY IN MY GENOSHAN ARMY, UNTIL HE DISCOVERED I WASN'T THE CHAMPION OF DEMOCRACY I PRETENDED TO BE.

SO HE TOOK TO THE HILLS, AND REPORTS HAVE IT THAT HE'S DECIDED TO START HIS OWN REVOLUTION--AND HAS A VENDETTA AGAINST ME.

A VENDETTA HE WILL NOT LIVE LONG ENOUGH TO CARRY OUT.

STORM AND JUBILEE--BEING HELD PRISONER IN DE PUNISHMENT BOXES 'CAUSE DE ESCAPE ATTEMPT FAILED.*

BUT OL' REMY GOT DE WAY OUT FOR DEM BOT'.

AND YOU, *CHERIE*, I THOUGHT 'BOUT YOU BEIN' LOCKED IN DE DARK--BEIN' CLAUSTROPHOBIC.

YOU GOT DE RARE *STRENGTH*, STORMY, ANYONE BUT YOU-- DEY CRACK UNDER DE STRAIN.

HOW YOU FEELIN' NOW, MADEMOISELLE?

STILL WEAK, GAMBIT. I WAS SO CLOSE TO LOSING IT...SO VERY CLOSE. THANK YOU.

REST YOUR HEAD NOW, *CHERIE*. REMY'S WIT' YOU.

NO--NO TIME FOR WEAKNESS.

THIS PLACE--THIS GENOSHA-- IS A *BLASPHEMY*...THE FINAL INSULT--THE FINAL INDIGNITY TOWARD OUR KIND!

NEVER HAVE I FELT SUCH *HATRED* TOWARD ANY PLACE!

BY THE GODDESS, THIS HORROR WILL *NOT* BE ALLOWED TO STAND!

I WILL WIPE THE FACE OF THIS ISLAND *CLEAN* OF ITS UGLINESS! I WILL SEE ITS EVIL *DESTROYED!*

WHOAH! SHE IS PUMPED!

SHE IS DE STORM, PETITE!

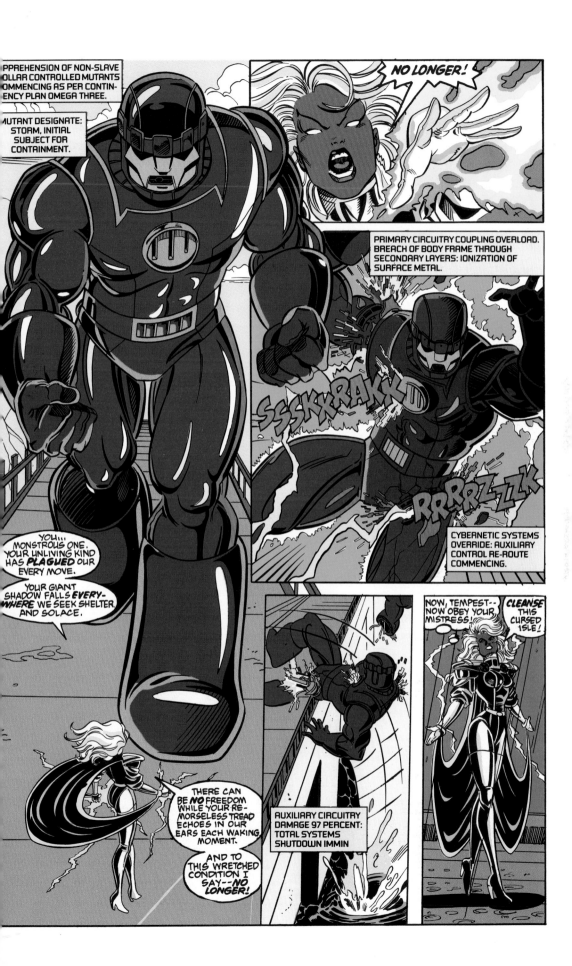